THE ODD SQUAD

BY ALLAN PLENDERLEITH

RAVETTE PUBLISHING

First published in 2002 by
Ravette Publishing Limited
Unit 3, Tristar Centre
Star Road, Partridge Green
West Sussex RH13 8RA

www.theoddsquad.co.uk

Printed in Malta by Gutenberg Press

ISBN: 1 84161 140 9

Hmmm....
"peanut"....
FUMP!

FART TYPE No.1

THE HOT ONE

MAKES NO SOUND BUT KILLS EVERYTHING IN A 12 METRE RADIUS.

FART TYPE No.2

THE RUMBLER

SOUNDS LIKE A DISTANT RUMBLE OF THUNDER. SMELL SEEPS OUT OVER SEVERAL HOURS. COMMONLY DONE BY OLD PEOPLE.

Storm's a comin!
RMBLRMBL!

FART TYPE No.3
THE SQUEAKY

HIGH-PITCHED,
LONG-LASTING,
NO SMELL.
COMMONLY DONE
BY WOMEN.

EEEEEEEP!!

FART TYPE No.4

THE RASPER

A SHORT SHARP BLAST BEST PERFORMED ON PLASTIC SEATS. GOOD FOR SCARING AWAY KIDS.

BRAAP!

FART TYPE No.5

THE SQUELCHER

FAST UNDERWEAR
CHANGE REQUIRED
IMMEDIATELY!

Uh oh!
THPPPPT.... SQUELCH!

FART TYPE No.6

THE TOILET BOWL BOOM

THE LOUDEST OF ALL FARTS MADE EVEN LOUDER BY THE EXCELLENT TOILET BOWL ACOUSTICS.

BOOM

FART TYPE No.7

THE SUPPRESSED SOFA FART

FART IS LET OFF INTO SOFA TO AVOID EMBARRASSMENT WHEN GUESTS ARE ROUND.

FUMMMMM!

FART TYPE No.8

THE MID-SEX BODY FART

DURING SEX, SWEATY BODIES BOUNCE TOGETHER TO PRODUCE THE HILARIOUS BODY FART.

FLAARP!
HA
HA
PAH
HA
HA
HA
HA

FART TYPE No.9

THE ACCIDENTAL FART

FART SLIPS OUT WHEN YOU LEAST EXPECT IT. USUALLY HAPPENS WHEN YOU'RE TRYING TO IMPRESS SOMEONE YOU FANCY.

Why don't you follow me into the bedroo-

FWARP!

FART TYPE No.10

THE JOGGER'S FART

FART COMES OUT IN SMALL BURSTS AS YOU RUN. MOST AMUSING.

TEE HEE!
FUMP!
FUMP!
FUMP!
FUMP!
FUMP!

ONE OF THE MANY DISADVANTAGES OF HAVING A FAT BUM IS FARTS CAN'T ESCAPE.

SHE'S GONNA BLOW!!
RUMBLE

ALTHOUGH HE
TRIED TO
BLAME HIS FARTS
ON THE DOG,
JEFF WASN'T
FOOLING ANYONE.

BAD DOG!

THE NEXT MORNING, MAUDE DIDN'T RECOGNISE HER DATE, AND HE HAD <u>SUCH</u> BAD BREATH!

ALTHOUGH AT THE TIME EVERYONE WAS DISTRAUGHT OVER THE TRAGIC EVENT, LATER EVERYONE WOULD AGREE THAT THE DOG FARTING ITSELF INTO THE FIRE WAS ACTUALLY BLOODY FUNNY.

FWOOM!
FARP!

FOR MAUDE, THE NOVELTY OF JEFF'S NIGHTLY 'HOVERING DUVET' TRICK HAD NOW WORN OFF.

FARP!
EEP!
FUMP!
TOOT!

NEVER BLOW OFF
WHILST IN THE
DOGGY POSITION.

TOOT!

BILLY WINS THE SWIMMING COMPETITION THANKS TO THAT VINDALOO THE NIGHT BEFORE.

THPPPPPPPPPPPPTTTTTTTTT!!!!!
!

AFTER SEEING THE
METHOD DAVE
USED TO FROTH
HIS MILK, JEFF
DECIDES
<u>NOT</u> TO HAVE A
CAPPUCCINO
AFTER ALL.

PLUP
PLOP
PLUP
PLUP

THAT CONDOM
THE CAT
SWALLOWED
LAST WEEK
FINALLY MAKES
AN APPEARANCE.

PUMP!

A FEW MORE WEEKS OF THIS SCAM, AND SANJIT'S JAGUAR WILL BE COMPLETELY PAID FOR.

THE BALTI HOUSE
Bathroom Fee £20
RUMBLE
SQUIRT!

UNFORTUNATELY,
BEING
CONSTIPATED
MEANT MAUDE'S
FARTS ONLY HAD
ONE WAY TO GO.

FWARH!!

TOO POOR TO PAY THE HEATING BILLS, LILY AND ALF ARE FORCED TO FIND OTHER WAYS TO KEEP WARM.

MORE!
MORE!
(cough
cough)
FWAAHH!

IN AN ATTEMPT
TO SMELL HIS
OWN FART,
JEFF BENDS BACK
TOO FAR.

SNAP!!

NEVER BLOW OFF
IN A G-STRING.

WHISTLE!

MAUDE WAS JUST
ABOUT TO SAY
HOW NICE THE
NEW JACUZZI
WAS, WHEN SHE
NOTICED
SOMETHING.

AAAHHH!

SOME MORNINGS MAUDE JUST COULDN'T BE BOTHERED DRIVING THE KIDS TO SCHOOL.

POOM!

JEFF STOOD
QUIETLY FACING
THE LIFT DOORS,
HOPING NO-ONE
HAD NOTICED
HE'D DROPPED A
HOT ONE.

JEFF AND
MAUDE VISIT THE
FAMOUS
SPHINCTER OF
EGYPT.

CLICK!

WHENEVER SHE BLOWS OFF LILY USES IT AS AN EXCUSE TO DO HER MARILYN MONROE IMPRESSION.

PWAM!
AP.

JEFF WAS
ALWAYS
EMBARRASSED
WHEN HIS
MOBILE WENT
OFF ON THE
TRAIN.

FARP!

JEFF HAD THE FEELING GOLDIE THE HAMSTER HAD A LITTLE TRAPPED WIND.

HELP ME!

WET FARTS ARE
BAD AT ANY TIME,
BUT WORSE IF
YOU'RE WEARING
SHORTS.

AAAAAAA!!
Aeeeeeee!
DRIP
SQUELCH
OOZE

BILLY HOPED
NO-ONE NOTICED
HE HAD TERRIBLE
WIND.

THE CURRY HOUSE'S FIERY REPUTATION SEEMED TO BE TRUE.

FART TIP NO. 1:

FOR MAXIMUM VOLUME, ALWAYS LET RIP ON A PLASTIC SEAT.

WAITING
ROOM
RASP!!!

FART TIP NO. 2:

WHEN LIGHTING FARTS, CLEAR THE ROOM OF ALL PETS.

FWOOM!

FART TIP NO. 3:

TRY PLAYING TUNES WITH FARTS BY PLACING A KAZOO BETWEEN YOUR CHEEKS.

Moon River?
TOOT!
TOOT!
TOOT!
Correct!

FART TIP NO. 4:

FOR MAXIMUM EFFECT, ALWAYS BLOW OFF IN AN ENCLOSED ENVIRONMENT.

AKH! Can't.... breathe....!

FART TIP NO. 5:

TO EXPERIENCE THE SPECIAL SCENT OF YOUR OWN PUMPS, TRY ATTACHING A SIMPLE PIECE OF HOSE TO YOUR BUM.

Hmmm....
"peanut"....
FUMP!

FART TIP NO. 6:

IF YOU FART IN THE BATH BE CAREFUL YOU DON'T FOLLOW THROUGH.

AAA!!

TYPES OF FARTER NO. 1:

THE 'SNEAKY' FARTER

SNEAKS UP IN STEALTH MODE AND LETS OFF A HOT ONE.

TYPES OF FARTER NO. 2:

THE 'ALL MOUTH NO TROUSERS' FARTER

GATHERS EVERYONE TO HEAR THEIR BIG FART, ONLY TO LET OUT A DISAPPOINTING SQUEAK.

EEP!

TYPES OF FARTER NO. 3:

THE 'THROWER'

CATCHES FART
WITH THEIR HAND
AND THROWS IT
IN YOUR FACE.
EVIL.

TYPES OF FARTER NO. 4

THE 'NEVER FARTS' FARTER

CLAIMS TO NEVER HAVE FARTED IN THEIR ENTIRE LIFE. WILL ONE DAY EXPLODE.

BANG!

TYPES OF FARTER NO. 5

THE 'MASTER BLASTER'

LIFTS LEG AS HIGH AS POSSIBLE AND LETS RIP, KNOCKING ORNAMENTS AND CHILDREN FOR SIX.

BRRAP!!

TYPES OF FARTER NO. 6

THE 'EMBARRASSED FARTER'

HOLDS IT IN UNTIL NO-ONE IN A 5 MILE RADIUS IS PRESENT.

FU

Other ODD SQUAD titles available...

The Odd Squad's Little Book of ... series

	ISBN	Price
Men	1 84161 093 3	£2.50
Sex	1 84161 095 X	£2.50
Women	1 84161 094 1	£2.50
Poo	1 84161 096 8	£2.50
Booze	1 84161 138 7	£2.50
X-Rated Cartoons	1 84161 141 7	£2.50
Oldies	1 84161 139 5	£2.50
The REAL Kama Sutra	1 84161 103 4	£3.99
The Odd Squad - Vol 1	1 85304 936 0	£3.99

Ordering.. *Please send a cheque/postal order in £ sterling, made payable to 'Ravette Publishing Ltd' for the cover price of the book/s and allow the following for postage and packing...*

UK & BFPO	*50p for the first book & 30p per book thereafter*
Europe & Eire	*£1.00 for the first book & 50p per book thereafter*
Rest of the world	*£1.80 for the first book & 80p per book thereafter*

Ravette Publishing Ltd.
Unit 3, Tristar Centre, Star Road, Partridge Green, West Sussex RH13 8RA